MORE I'M THROUGH! WHAT CAN I DO?

Editor: Regina Kim
Designer/Production: Rebekah O. Lewis
Cover Illustrator: Karl Edwards
Cover Designer: Barbara Peterson
Art Director: Moonhee Pak
Project Director: Betsy Morris, PhD

Table of Contents

Introduction

More I'm Through! What Can I Do? is a one-stop resource that addresses this all-too-familiar question teachers hear from students who finish early. The high-interest, ready-to-use puzzles, riddles, brainteasers, and mazes can be completed with minimal teacher assistance and help sharpen language arts, math, creative thinking, and critical thinking skills. This new series is a follow-up to our best-selling titles *I'm Through! What Can I Do?*

GETTING STARTED

Use any of the following suggestions to create a simple, structured environment that allows students to access these activities independently and keeps busy classrooms running smoothly.

1. Create individual student packets using all of the activity pages. Have students keep the packets in their desks and complete pages if they finish their assigned work early.

2. Create smaller packets by content areas (language arts and math) to use at centers. Store each set of packets in a file folder. Attach a class list to the outside of each folder. Have students cross out their names after they complete the packet.

3. Use activity pages individually as
   - supplements to specific lessons
   - homework assignments
   - substitute teacher's helpers
   - three-minute transition activities
   - morning warm-up or after-lunch refocusing activities

HELPFUL TIPS TO FREE YOUR TIME
   - Allow students to consult classmates to figure out puzzles.
   - Encourage students to correct each other's work.
   - Place copies of the answer key in an accessible area for students to pull as needed for self-correction.
   - Give students copies of the Student Recording Sheet (page 4) to keep track of completed activity pages. Have students color in or check off each activity after it is completed.

However you choose to use the activity pages, let *More I'm Through! What Can I Do?* assist you in establishing a constructive and productive classroom environment.

Name: _____

Keep track of your work by filling in the box after completing the activity.

p. 5	p. 6	p. 7	p. 8	p. 9	p. 10	p. 11	p. 12	p. 13	p. 14
p. 15	p.16	p. 17	p. 18	p. 19	p. 20	p. 21	p. 22	p. 23	p. 24
p. 25	p. 26	p. 27	p. 28	p. 29	p. 30	p. 31	p. 32	p. 33	p. 34
p. 35	p. 36	p. 37	p. 38	p. 39	p. 40	p. 41	p. 42	p. 43	p. 44
p. 45	p. 46	p. 47	p. 48	p. 49	p. 50	p. 51	p. 52	p. 53	p. 54
p. 55	p. 56	p. 57	p. 58	p. 59	p. 60	p. 61	p. 62	p. 63	p. 64
p. 65	p. 66	p. 67	p. 68	p.69	p. 70	p. 71	p. 72	p. 73	p. 74
p. 75	p. 76	p. 77	p. 78	p. 79	p. 80	p. 81	p. 82	p. 83	p. 84
p. 85	p. 86	p. 87	p. 88	p. 89	p. 90				

More I'm Through! What Can I Do? Grade 4 © 2008 Creative Teaching Press

Word Maker #1

How many words can you find in the Word Maker square? There are more than 50 words!

Rules to remember:

- The words you find must have 3 or more letters.
- From any beginning letter, build a word by going left, right, up, down, or diagonally. (A single word may go in more than one direction.)
- You may not skip a square! Each letter in a word must touch the squares before and after it.
- The same letter square <u>can</u> be used more than once in a word, but it cannot be used twice in a row.
- The star can count for any letter, and it can be used twice in a row.
- Proper nouns (e.g., *Harry*) are not allowed.

s	t	a
y	★	n
h	a	w

_____   _____   _____

_____   _____   _____

_____   _____   _____

_____   _____   _____

_____   _____   _____

Word Maker #2

How many words can you find in the Word Maker square? There are more than 50 words!

Rules to remember:

- The words you find must have 3 or more letters.
- From any beginning letter, build a word by going left, right, up, down, or diagonally. (A single word may go in more than one direction.)
- You may not skip a square! Each letter in a word must touch the squares before and after it.
- The same letter square <u>can</u> be used more than once in a word, but it cannot be used twice in a row.
- The star can count for any letter, and it can be used twice in a row.
- Proper nouns (e.g., *Harry*) are not allowed.

y	e	k
o	v	n
m	★	a

_____ _____ _____

_____ _____ _____

_____ _____ _____

_____ _____ _____

_____ _____ _____

More I'm Through! What Can I Do? Grade 4 © 2008 Creative Teaching Press

Word Maker #3

How many words can you find in the Word Maker square? There are more than 50 words!

Rules to remember:

- The words you find must have 3 or more letters.
- From any beginning letter, build a word by going left, right, up, down, or diagonally. (A single word may go in more than one direction.)
- You may not skip a square! Each letter in a word must touch the squares before and after it.
- The same letter square <u>can</u> be used more than once in a word, but it cannot be used twice in a row.
- The star can count for any letter, and it can be used twice in a row.
- Proper nouns (e.g., *Harry*) are not allowed.

z	★	a	s
d	u	l	a
i	e	r	k
h	s	e	g

_____   _____   _____

_____   _____   _____

_____   _____   _____

_____   _____   _____

_____   _____   _____

More I'm Through! What Can I Do? Grade 4 © 2008 Creative Teaching Press

Word Maker #4

How many words can you find in the Word Maker square? There are more than 50 words!

Rules to remember:

- The words you find must have 3 or more letters.
- From any beginning letter, build a word by going left, right, up, down, or diagonally. (A single word may go in more than one direction.)
- You may not skip a square! Each letter in a word must touch the squares before and after it.
- The same letter square <u>can</u> be used more than once in a word, but it cannot be used twice in a row.
- The star can count for any letter, and it can be used twice in a row.
- Proper nouns (e.g., *Harry*) are not allowed.

h	l	o	b
y	c	o	m
e	★	l	s
o	b	x	v

_____   _____   _____

_____   _____   _____

_____   _____   _____

_____   _____   _____

_____   _____   _____

More I'm Through! What Can I Do? Grade 4 © 2008 Creative Teaching Press

Magic Word Scramble

Unscramble the words related to magic. Then complete the sentence below.

n a d w = _____

e s p l s l = _____

z i a d r w = _____

f w p r e o u l = _____

a n v i h s = _____

a m c a i g n i = _____

c o n e u r j = _____

d s p i a e a r p = _____

u m i y s t r o e s = _____

a e n n c t e d h = _____

Have a _____ time!

a a i l c m g

Natural Disasters
Word Scramble

Unscramble the names of these natural disasters.

a r d o t n o   = _____

d a l l i d s e n   = _____

p e i t u r n o   = _____

n v c o a o l   = _____

n u s a i m t   = _____

a e h v l c a a n   = _____

r u e t a e q k h a   = _____

o y t n h o p   = _____

z l b a d i r z   = _____

r c u h i a r e n   = _____

Learn safety _____ .

n t e r p s a c u o i

More I'm Through! What Can I Do? Grade 4 © 2008 Creative Teaching Press

Secret Word #1

o	a	l	c	i	u	s	n	p	b	i	t

Look at the letters in the box above. Use them to make as many words as you can. Write the words in the matching box. Then try to identify the secret word that can be spelled using all of the letters.

3-letter words	4-letter words
_____ _____	_____ _____
_____ _____	_____ _____
_____ _____	_____ _____
_____ _____	_____ _____
_____ _____	_____ _____

5-letter words	More than 5 letters
_____ _____	_____ _____
_____ _____	_____ _____
_____ _____	_____ _____
_____ _____	_____ _____
_____ _____	_____ _____

The secret word is _____.

Secret Word #2

o	n	i	v	r	r	c	t	s	a	o	e	l

Look at the letters in the box above. Use them to make as many words as you can. Write the words in the matching box. Then try to identify the secret word that can be spelled using all of the letters.

3-letter words

_____ _____

_____ _____

_____ _____

_____ _____

_____ _____

_____ _____

4-letter words

_____ _____

_____ _____

_____ _____

_____ _____

_____ _____

_____ _____

5-letter words

_____ _____

_____ _____

_____ _____

_____ _____

_____ _____

More than 5 letters

_____ _____

_____ _____

_____ _____

_____ _____

_____ _____

The secret word is _____.

More I'm Through! What Can I Do? Grade 4 © 2008 Creative Teaching Press

Gingerbread Cookies

How many words can you make using the letters in **gingerbread cookies**? Write the words on the lines below!

- Your words must use 3 or more letters.
- Your words can use letters in any order from **gingerbread cookies**.
- You may only use each letter as many times as it appears in the word. (For example, you may not have a word with 4 **e**'s because there are only 3 **e**'s in **gingerbread cookies**.)
- No proper nouns!

Scoring:

Three-letter word	= 1 point
Four-letter word	= 2 points
Five-letter word	= 3 points
Six-letter word	= 4 points
More than six letters	= 5 points

_____   _____   _____

_____   _____   _____

_____   _____   _____

_____   _____   _____

_____   _____   _____

_____   _____   _____

_____   _____   _____

_____   _____   _____

Number of words I found: _____   **Points:** _____

More I'm Through! What Can I Do? Grade 4 © 2008 Creative Teaching Press

Name: _____   Date: _____

Banana Cream Pie

How many words can you make using the letters in **banana cream pie**? Write the words on the lines below!

Rules to remember:

- Your words must use 3 or more letters.
- Your words can use letters in any order from **banana cream pie**.
- You may only use each letter as many times as it appears in the word. (For example, you may not have a word with 3 **e**'s because there are only 2 **e**'s in **banana cream pie**.)
- No proper nouns!

Scoring:

Three-letter word	= 1 point
Four-letter word	= 2 points
Five-letter word	= 3 points
Six-letter word	= 4 points
More than six letters	= 5 points

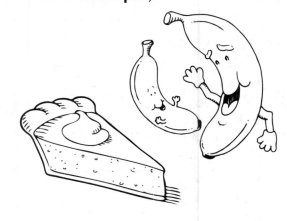

_____ _____ _____

_____ _____ _____

_____ _____ _____

_____ _____ _____

_____ _____ _____

_____ _____ _____

_____ _____ _____

Number of words I found: _____   **Points:** _____

More I'm Through! What Can I Do? Grade 4 © 2008 Creative Teaching Press

Super Scramble

Scramble the letters, and use them to write a new word on each line. The first one has been done for you.

rings	grins
hoes	_____
eats	_____
tabs	_____
parts	_____
veil	_____
mean	_____
male	_____
sever	_____

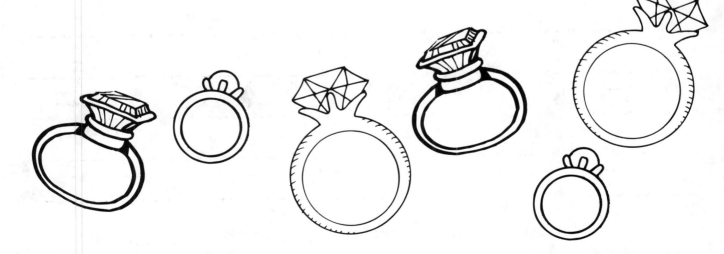

Break the Code #1

Find the answer to the riddle by writing a letter for each picture symbol on the lines below. The first letter has been done for you.

A	B	C	D	E	F	G	H	I	J	K	L	M
●	◄	☯	□	★	☺	◉	&	☾	♊	☼	▶	✓

N	O	P	Q	R	S	T	U	V	W	X	Y	Z
⚑	👍	◗	✿	⊠	≈	♈	♓	♦	✦	❖	✺	➤

What do cows do for fun?

♈   &   ★   ✺   ◉   ♈

T __ __ __   __ __   __ __

♈   &   ★   ✓   ♦   ☾   ★   ≈

__ __ __ __ __ _ __   __ __ __ __ .

More I'm Through! What Can I Do? Grade 4 © 2008 Creative Teaching Press

Break the Code #2

Find the answer to the riddle by writing a letter for each picture symbol on the lines below. The first letter has been done for you.

A	B	C	D	E	F	G	H	I	J	K	L	M
●	◄	☯	□	★	☺	◉	&	☾	♊	☼	►	✓

N	O	P	Q	R	S	T	U	V	W	X	Y	Z
⚑	👍	♦	❀	⊠	≈	♈	♓	◆	◇	❖	❋	◄

What do you call cheese that is not yours?

N _ _ _ _

_ _ _ _ _ _ !

Break the Code #3

Find the answer to the riddle by writing a letter for each picture symbol on the lines below. The first letter has been done for you.

A	B	C	D	E	F	G	H	I	J	K	L	M
●	◄	☯	□	★	☺	◉	&	☾	Ⅱ	☼	➤	✔

N	O	P	Q	R	S	T	U	V	W	X	Y	Z
⚑	👍	◗	✿	⊠	♒	♈	♓	◆	◇	❖	✺	◄

Where do polar bears vote?

♈ & ★   ⚑ 👍 ⊠ ♈ &

T __ __   __ __ __ __ __

◗ 👍 ➤ ➤

__ __ __ __ !

More I'm Through! What Can I Do? Grade 4 © 2008 Creative Teaching Press

Baby Animals Crossword

Directions: Write the name of the offspring for each animal to complete the crossword puzzle. Use books, the Internet, or other reference materials to help you.

Across

1. deer
4. eagle
5. dog
6. giraffe
8. lion
9. swan
11. hog
13. cat
14. bobcat

Down

2. otter
3. zebra
5. turkey
7. fish
10. goose
12. ostrich

Just for Fun

Write the name of the offspring for each of these animals. Use an encyclopedia and other reference materials if you need help.

a. hawk _____

b. whale _____

c. donkey _____

d. kangaroo _____

e. rhinoceros _____

More I'm Through! What Can I Do? Grade 4 © 2008 Creative Teaching Press

Step Up #1

The object of this puzzle is to change one word into another by changing only one letter at a time. You cannot change the order of the letters.

1.
d i m e

_____dame_____ (another word for lady)

_____ (number on the calendar)

l a t e

2.
b e e s

_____ (another word for looks)

_____ (fasten by stitches)

s a w s

bees

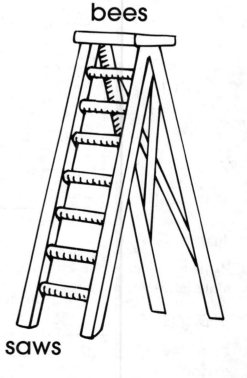

saws

3.
c e l l

_____ (use a phone)

_____ (a spherical toy)

b a l d

More I'm Through! What Can I Do? Grade 4 © 2008 Creative Teaching Press

Step Up #2

The object of this puzzle is to change one word into another by changing only one letter at a time. You cannot change the order of the letters.

1.   s o r t

_____ (muscle pain)

_____ (small skin opening)

_____ (a ship dock)

p a r t

2.   b l o w

_____ (not fast)

_____ (to move in a stream)

_____ (a defect)

f l a t

3.   t i r e d

_____ (passed a way)

_____ (colored fabric)

_____ (looked at)

e y e s

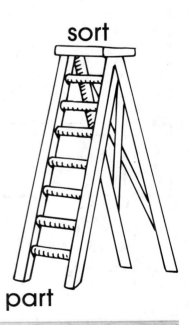

sort

part

Name: _____ Date: _____

Water Sports Word Search

The 16 words listed below are in the puzzle **horizontally**, **vertically**, **diagonally**, and **backwards**. Can you find all of them? Circle or lightly shade the words as you find them.

G	R	R	A	M	P	G	N	I	M	M	I	W	S	S	G	S	X	M	J
Z	N	Q	A	G	D	A	D	G	H	P	S	S	K	U	N	S	T	R	E
U	G	I	M	F	K	L	R	S	N	R	Z	I	G	O	I	Z	E	F	T
U	W	H	U	G	T	G	C	A	A	I	I	Q	R	W	K	T	L	V	D
X	Z	D	N	O	N	I	D	O	S	N	W	K	F	F	A	H	G	J	V
K	B	O	H	I	N	I	N	N	G	A	E	O	L	W	Y	Z	N	E	L
O	D	Q	L	Q	K	A	P	G	J	L	I	J	R	Y	A	C	I	H	W
H	N	I	P	R	B	Z	C	E	I	K	X	L	T	H	K	A	B	K	J
K	A	Z	S	U	R	F	I	N	G	V	H	F	I	Y	S	C	U	B	A
S	P	X	T	D	R	Q	G	X	P	N	R	J	C	N	V	W	T	O	N
F	Q	O	Q	V	Z	W	X	O	H	J	F	O	Z	P	G	I	S	U	S
K	P	I	L	K	W	B	P	R	S	L	R	Y	W	T	X	N	D	Z	I
O	J	U	S	O	E	H	B	C	S	Z	I	M	H	C	N	D	P	N	C
B	T	G	N	I	E	O	N	A	C	V	M	G	N	Z	A	S	F	G	H
V	J	S	N	P	A	E	D	U	M	U	J	C	V	G	R	U	I	M	E
D	W	R	K	I	T	R	L	Y	R	V	O	F	M	U	S	R	S	U	V
A	S	F	N	H	B	U	G	V	I	N	Q	F	V	J	H	F	H	W	I
V	J	R	E	Q	E	Y	R	U	F	J	N	V	L	S	U	I	I	L	N
C	Z	A	R	W	A	K	E	B	O	A	R	D	I	N	G	N	N	F	F
G	N	I	V	I	D	W	Q	F	A	J	T	G	Y	O	N	G	G	D	V

CANOEING	PARASAILING	SCUBA	SWIMMING
DIVING	POLO	SKIING	TUBING
FISHING	RAFTING	SNORKELING	WAKEBOARDING
KAYAKING	ROWING	SURFING	WIND SURFING

More I'm Through! What Can I Do? Grade 4 © 2008 Creative Teaching Press

Insect Word Search

The 17 insect words listed below are hidden in the puzzle **horizontally**, **vertically**, **diagonally**, and **backwards**. Can you find all of them? Circle or lightly shade the words as you find them.

T	L	M	W	I	D	P	D	T	M	N	B	S	D	W	U
E	X	O	S	K	E	L	E	T	O	N	E	V	I	G	S
U	A	B	M	T	Z	V	L	I	D	I	E	W	H	P	D
H	Z	R	G	O	E	V	T	D	N	R	T	H	P	I	P
Z	C	M	T	R	L	A	S	O	K	E	L	M	A	B	J
A	I	A	M	H	T	T	L	Y	C	P	E	V	O	R	C
W	V	I	O	S	R	O	I	H	F	E	E	L	E	R	S
G	N	R	E	R	C	O	R	N	N	L	C	L	E	U	O
B	V	F	A	E	K	Y	P	V	G	L	K	W	A	E	T
Q	N	N	F	L	S	C	L	O	P	E	R	A	O	B	I
I	E	Y	S	A	W	Y	O	I	D	N	W	Z	J	C	U
X	B	W	L	X	T	Y	Y	C	K	T	E	Z	E	Y	Q
D	W	I	R	F	F	H	T	L	N	O	R	T	O	P	S
Z	S	Y	L	F	R	E	T	T	U	B	Q	R	E	U	O
W	G	H	J	O	C	W	F	K	N	V	A	L	M	C	M
C	N	P	H	B	J	D	G	S	D	Y	A	F	Q	R	B
I	I	L	V	H	I	K	F	M	V	X	M	R	A	W	S
U	W	T	U	T	M	K	Q	O	W	A	Z	P	C	T	W

APHID
ARTHROPOD
BEETLE
BUTTERFLY
CHRYSALIS

COCKROACH
COLONIES
EXOSKELETON
FEELERS
INFESTATION

LARVA
MOLTING
MOSQUITO
REPELLENT
SWARM

VERMIN
WINGS

More Than the Eye

Count how many squares are in the grid below. **Hint:** (There are more than 30!)

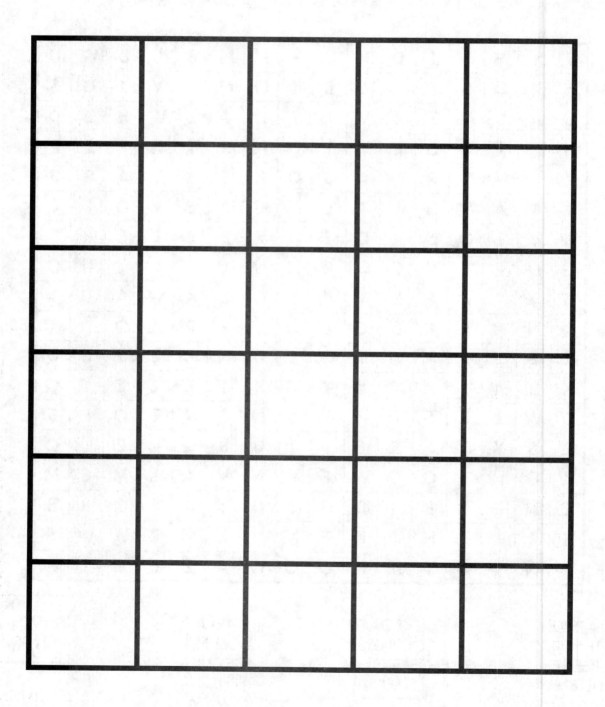

There are _____ squares.

More I'm Through! What Can I Do? Grade 4 © 2008 Creative Teaching Press

Negative and Positive Maze

Follow the math maze from "Start" to "End." Solve the addition and subtraction problems as you go. Write the final answer in the starburst.

						Start
=	⁻9		⁺4	–	⁻8	⁺10
End	+		–		+	–
	⁻8		⁻1		⁻2	⁺3
	–		+		–	+
	⁺4		⁻6		⁺6	⁻7
	+		+		–	+
	⁺5		⁺2		⁺8	⁻5
	–		–		+	–
	0	+	⁻9		⁺6	+	⁻2

Negative and Positive Path

Follow the math maze by solving the addition and subtraction problems along the way. Write the final answer in the bubble.

	=	⁻8		⁻6	+	⁻3		+11	Start
End		−		+		+		−	
		+4		+8		⁻1		+4	
		+		+		−		+	
		⁻1		+1		+12		⁻8	
		+		+		+		+	
		⁻1		⁻8		⁻5		⁻6	
		+		+		−		+	
		+9	+	⁻5		+7	+	⁻2	

Computation Maze

Follow the math maze by solving the addition, subtraction, multiplication, and division problems along the way. Write the final answer in the bubble.

					Start
=	12	4	+	3	10
	X	X		+	X
	9	2		3	8
	−	÷		+	÷
	16	10		6	2
	+	X		÷	+
	5	12		5	5
	÷	+		−	÷
	21	−	10	7	X	9

End

Amazing Pathways

Begin with the "start" number. Move vertically or horizontally through the maze, one square at a time. Use addition or subtraction to reach the "finish" number at the end of the path. (You may need to try several paths before you find the right one.) Draw a line to show your path. No square may be used more than once, and some squares won't be used at all. You must end with the total in the "finish" box.

START 1	11	25	12	36	
	35	10	38	4	
	24	11	3	8	
	14	22	13	3	100 FINISH

START 100	8	16	9	14	
	12	27	32	11	
	17	3	6	26	
	4	13	7	17	1 FINISH

START 8	23	18	42	16	
	35	19	14	62	
	29	31	27	58	
	40	9	54	36	222 FINISH

More I'm Through! What Can I Do? Grade 4 © 2008 Creative Teaching Press

Find Math Words

The 30 math words at the bottom of this paper are hidden in the puzzle **horizontally**, **vertically**, **diagonally**, and **backwards**. Can you find all of them? Circle or lightly shade the words as you find them.

A	E	C	D	Y	W	D	I	F	F	E	R	E	N	C	E	P
B	E	Q	U	A	T	I	O	N	A	X	E	N	P	F	C	X
K	T	U	S	B	B	G	D	D	E	C	I	M	A	L	O	M
V	G	Y	M	U	D	I	V	I	D	E	N	D	Z	G	M	N
A	E	G	U	R	M	T	A	M	H	I	J	I	D	H	P	P
Z	P	R	O	B	A	B	I	L	I	T	Y	V	Y	U	U	Q
H	O	F	P	G	X	C	L	Q	U	O	T	I	E	N	T	Z
I	S	H	P	R	I	M	E	A	A	P	O	S	V	D	A	E
J	I	S	O	M	V	W	Q	P	T	Z	M	I	B	R	T	O
L	T	R	S	T	W	N	O	S	R	O	Z	O	M	E	I	R
I	I	D	I	V	I	S	O	R	O	M	T	N	I	D	O	Y
H	V	G	T	Q	F	F	N	E	G	A	T	I	V	E	N	L
X	E	D	E	N	O	M	I	N	A	T	O	R	L	T	K	Q
U	T	H	O	U	S	A	N	D	E	F	I	L	D	V	I	S
V	O	O	M	B	O	S	I	I	B	R	E	S	T	R	K	D
A	D	E	M	A	N	I	P	U	L	A	T	I	V	E	J	R
K	M	A	A	G	O	B	S	S	U	C	F	V	G	M	H	T
M	U	L	T	I	P	L	I	C	A	T	I	O	N	A	C	B
C	L	G	H	B	E	Q	U	A	L	I	D	L	F	I	B	G
S	T	E	N	O	R	C	Z	K	V	O	Q	W	R	N	O	U
R	I	B	D	Z	C	W	M	A	T	N	S	I	P	D	N	H
C	P	R	A	D	E	S	T	I	M	A	T	E	S	E	B	J
D	L	A	B	A	N	O	O	N	V	L	M	K	Q	R	W	V
E	E	W	X	G	T	H	Y	J	K	Y	R	O	T	C	A	F

ALGEBRA	DIVIDEND	FACTOR	MULTIPLICATION	PROBABILITY
COMPUTATION	DIVISION	FRACTION	NEGATIVE	QUOTIENT
DECIMAL	DIVISOR	HUNDRED	OPPOSITE	REMAINDER
DENOMINATOR	EQUAL	MANIPULATIVE	PERCENT	SUM
DIFFERENCE	EQUATION	MATH	POSITIVE	THOUSAND
DIGIT	ESTIMATE	MULTIPLE	PRIME	TOTAL

Apple Seed Solutions

Johnny Appleseed planted apple seeds in Ohio and other parts of midwestern America. Solve the problems to learn his real name. Find the letter that matches each answer and write it on the line.

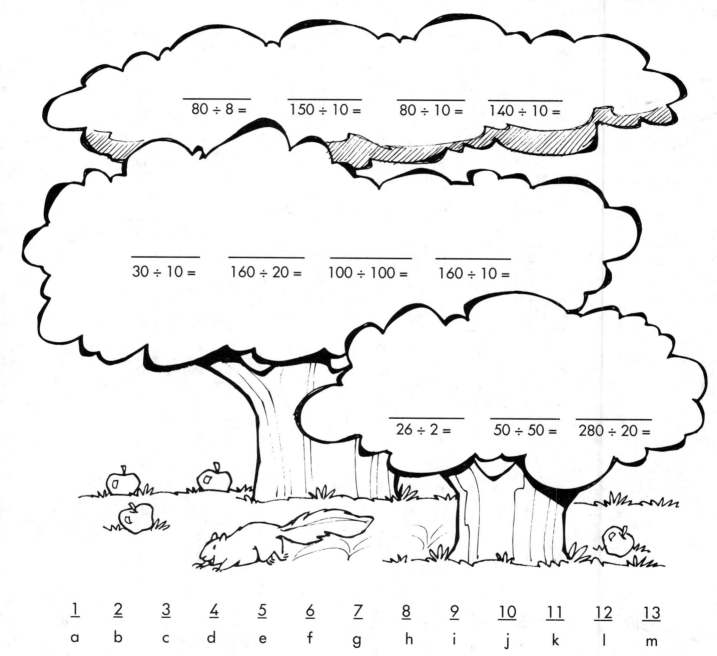

$80 \div 8 =$ _____ $150 \div 10 =$ _____ $80 \div 10 =$ _____ $140 \div 10 =$ _____

$30 \div 10 =$ _____ $160 \div 20 =$ _____ $100 \div 100 =$ _____ $160 \div 10 =$ _____

$26 \div 2 =$ _____ $50 \div 50 =$ _____ $280 \div 20 =$ _____

1	2	3	4	5	6	7	8	9	10	11	12	13
a	b	c	d	e	f	g	h	i	j	k	l	m

14	15	16	17	18	19	20	21	22	23	24	25	26
n	o	p	q	r	s	t	u	v	w	x	y	z

More I'm Through! What Can I Do? Grade 4 © 2008 Creative Teaching Press

Inventor

This mystery man found over 300 uses for the peanut. Solve the problems to learn his name. Find the letter that matches each answer and write it on the line.

___	___	___	___	___	___
1 x 7	35 ÷ 7	5 + 5 + 5	54 ÷ 3	16 - 9	100 ÷ 20

___	___	___	___	___	___	___	___	___	___
11 + 12	88 ÷ 88	23 - 4	72 ÷ 9	3 x 3 x 1	2 + 0 + 12	(40 + 2) ÷ 6	10 x 2	30 - 15	7 + 4 + 3

___	___	___	___	___	___
(32 + 4) ÷ 12	8 - 7	5 + 13	11 x 2	12 - 7	3 x 6

<u>1</u>	<u>2</u>	<u>3</u>	<u>4</u>	<u>5</u>	<u>6</u>	<u>7</u>	<u>8</u>	<u>9</u>	<u>10</u>	<u>11</u>	<u>12</u>	<u>13</u>
a	b	c	d	e	f	g	h	i	j	k	l	m

<u>14</u>	<u>15</u>	<u>16</u>	<u>17</u>	<u>18</u>	<u>19</u>	<u>20</u>	<u>21</u>	<u>22</u>	<u>23</u>	<u>24</u>	<u>25</u>	<u>26</u>
n	o	p	q	r	s	t	u	v	w	x	y	z

Find a Number

A.

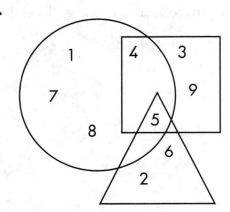

I am an even number.

I am less than 5.

I am in the square.

What number am I? _____

B.

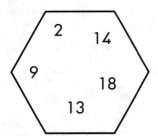

I am an even number.

I am larger than 10.

I am not in the triangle.

I am in the square.

I am also in the hexagon.

What number am I? _____

Find a Rule

Directions: Look at each set of input and output numbers to figure out what rule was used to change the input numbers to the output numbers. (Concentrate on one problem at a time.) Use the rule to find the missing output numbers. Write the rule symbolically using ■ for input and ▲ for output. The rule to get from input and output must be written as an equation with at least one operation sign and an equals sign (see sample problem).

Sample Problem

■ Input	▲ Output
2	6
4	20
5	30
6	**42**
7	**56**
1	**2**

Rule: ■ x ■ + ■ = ▲

1.

■ Input	▲ Output
2	2
8	5
6	4
4	?
0	?
10	?

Rule:

2.

■ Input	▲ Output
2	7
3	26
0	-1
4	?
5	?
6	?

Rule:

3.

■ Input	▲ Output
7	3
5	2
3	1
9	?
1	?
11	?

Rule:

4.

■ Input	▲ Output
12	4
24	7
4	2
16	?
20	?
0	?

Rule:

5.

■ Input	▲ Output
1	3
2	8
3	15
5	?
7	?
10	?

Rule:

Doughnuts

Read about the people who came to Mrs. Pfeiffer's bakery. Then solve the problems.

- Mrs. Pfeiffer makes the most delicious doughnuts around! This morning she put out trays of doughnuts.
- Mrs. Kimmel was the first customer. She bought two dozen doughnuts.
- Mr. Hoff came in next. He bought half the doughnuts that were left.
- Mrs. Pitt came in next. She bought half the doughnuts that were left.
- Mr. Norquist arrived next. He bought five doughnuts.
- There were seven doughnuts left.

How many doughnuts did each of the customers buy?

Mrs. Kimmel _____   Mrs. Pitt _____

Mr. Hoff _____   Mr. Norquist _____

How many doughnuts were on Mrs. Pfeiffer's trays this morning? _____

More I'm Through! What Can I Do? Grade 4 © 2008 Creative Teaching Press

Name: _____ Date: _____

It All Adds Up #1

In these two magic squares, each column and row adds up to 12. Using numbers 0 through 8, fill in the missing numbers. You may only use a number once.

7		3
	4	8
		1

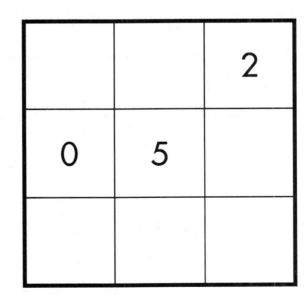

		2
0	5	

It All Adds Up #2

In this magic square, each column and row adds up to 34. Using numbers 1 through 16, fill in the missing numbers.

16		2	13
	10	11	
9			12
	15		

It All Adds Up #3

In this magic square, every row, column, and mini-grid must contain the numbers 1 through 6.
Fill in the missing numbers. Each number should only appear once in every row, column, or mini-grid.

2	1			4	3
		6	2		
		3	4		
3	4			5	6

It All Adds Up #4

In this magic square, every row, column, and mini-grid must contain the numbers 1 through 6.
Fill in the missing numbers. Each number should only appear once in every row, column, or mini-grid.

		2	4		
4					2
		6		3	
	4			6	
1					6
		3	5		

More I'm Through! What Can I Do? Grade 4 © 2008 Creative Teaching Press

It All Adds Up #5

In this magic square, every row, column, and mini-grid must contain the numbers 1 through 6.
Fill in the missing numbers. Each number should only appear once in every row, column, or mini-grid.

		1	6		
6					1
	1			6	
	5			3	
4					5
		5	4		

It All Adds Up #6

In this magic square, every row, column, and mini-grid must contain the numbers 1 through 9.
Fill in the missing numbers. Each number should only appear once in every row, column, and mini-grid.

				5		3		
	8	1	4		3	5	9	
			2		6			
7		5		3		4		8
		8		4		2		
2		4		1		6		7
			3		7			
	5	9	1		4	8	7	
		6		8		1		

Name: _____ Date: _____

It All Adds Up #7

In this magic square, every row, column, and mini-grid must contain the numbers 1 through 9.
Fill in the missing numbers. Each number should only appear once in every row, column, and mini-grid.

1								4
		3	6	1	8	9		
	2	7				6	1	
		8	1	6	9	4		
		1	2		7	3		
		6	8	5	3	1		
	1	5				7	3	
		2	3	7	6	5		
7								9

It All Adds Up #8

In this magic square, every row, column, and mini-grid must contain the numbers 1 through 9. Fill in the missing numbers. Each number should only appear once in every row, column, and mini-grid.

	7			6			2	
		3	2	9	7	5		
		6	5		4	3		
	6	8				7	1	
1		7				9		5
	9	5				2	8	
		4	8		2	1		
		1	3	5	6	4		
	5			1			3	

More I'm Through! What Can I Do? Grade 4 © 2008 Creative Teaching Press

Ice Cream Scoops

Using the four numbers on the ice cream scoops, what is…

1. the smallest number you can make? _____

2. the biggest number you can make? _____

3. the sum of middle numbers? _____

4. the number you get when you subtract the second
   number from the third number? _____

5. the sum of the last two numbers divided by the first number? _____

6. the sum of the even numbers? _____

7. the product of the first and third numbers? _____

8. the product of all four numbers? _____

9. the smallest number you can make that is still divisible by 4? _____

Taxi Numbers

Using the four numbers on the taxi signs, what is…

1. the smallest number you can make? _____

2. the biggest number you can make? _____

3. the sum of the last two numbers? _____

4. the number you get when you subtract the
    first from the second number? _____

5. the sum of the last two numbers divided by the first number? _____

6. the sum of the odd numbers? _____

7. the product of the first and last numbers? _____

8. the product of the last three numbers divided by 10? _____

9. the smallest number you can make that is still divisible by 2? _____

More I'm Through! What Can I Do? Grade 4 © 2008 Creative Teaching Press

See-Saw Solutions

Read each group of words. Add one more item to the see-saw so the ideas balance.
In the box below, write the category name! The first one is done for you.

1.
| jet |
| airplane |

kite
helicopter

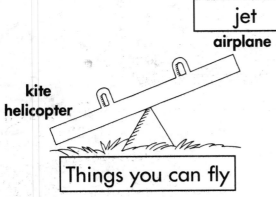

Things you can fly

2.
| centimeters |

inches
feet

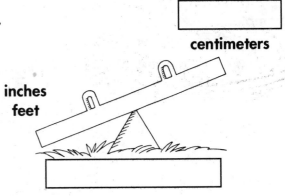

3.
ears

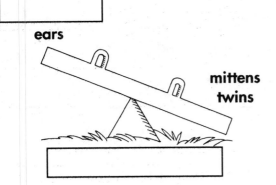

mittens
twins

4.
planets
asteroids

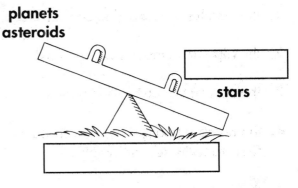

stars

5.
| cake |

pie
ice cream

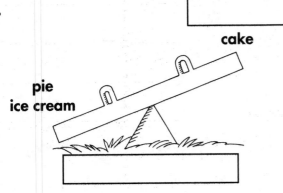

6.
bat

helmet
baseball glove

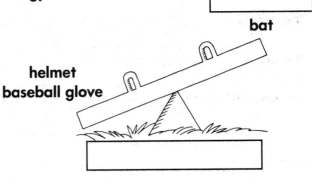

What's Missing?

Look at each series of words below. Figure out what the pattern is and add a word that continues the pattern. Then explain why your word is correct.

Example:

all, ban, cat, den, __egg__

Why? ___The next word must be a three-letter word that begins with the letter **e**.___

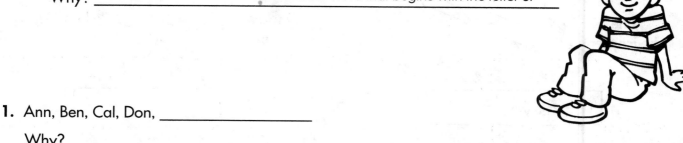

1. Ann, Ben, Cal, Don, _____

   Why? _____

2. a, an, act, able, _____

   Why? _____

3. a, by, cut, deer, _____

   Why? _____

4. ant, dent, glint, jaunt, _____

   Why? _____

5. tattle, stencil, replied, question, _____

   Why? _____

6. Al, Carl, Fran, Jarod, _____

   Why? _____

More I'm Through! What Can I Do? Grade 4 © 2008 Creative Teaching Press

Elimination

Read each set of items. Cross out the one that does not belong in the same category as the rest. Explain why it does not belong.

1. baseball   tennis   throw   football

_____

2. bedroom   building   dining room   kitchen

_____

3. wet   coffee   water   tea

_____

4. Bush   Washington   Adams   Perot

_____

5. Eriksson   Magellan   Hudson   Aldrich

_____

6. license   subscription   prescription   menu

_____

7. balloon   bicycle   raft   ball

_____

8. concrete   fur   steel   diamond

_____

9. frustrated   happy   melancholy   smile

_____

Name: _____ Date: _____

Favorite Sports

Fill in the deductive logic puzzle by reading each clue. When you reach some information that tells you a person doesn't like a certain sport, then put an "X" in that box. When you make an inference about what sport each person does play based on the facts and elimination, then color in that box. If a box is colored to represent "yes," then all other boxes in that column and row should have an "X" in them.

	Pauli	Bob	Deanne	Paul
soccer				
basketball				
tennis				
volleyball				

Clues to base your inferences on:

- To prepare for his sport, Bob runs two miles every day.
- Deanne's team is so good that they often end up with a final score that breaks 100!
- The person who uses a racket in her sport practices every day.
- Paul loves to play his sport on the beach.

More I'm Through! What Can I Do? Grade 4 © 2008 Creative Teaching Press

Which Bicycle?

Melanie, Leanne, Mark, and Susan all got new bicycles for Christmas. Each one has a different colored bicycle. The bicycles are yellow, red, white, and green. Use the clues to match each child with the correct bicycle.

- Melanie does not have a red or yellow bike.
- Mark's bike is the color of his eyes.
- The color of Leanne's bike would be listed last in the dictionary (out of these colors).

	Yellow	Red	White	Green
Melanie				
Leanne				
Mark				
Susan				

More I'm Through! What Can I Do? Grade 4 © 2008 Creative Teaching Press

Solving Puzzles

A. Alan, Jerry, Dean, and Carol did reports on tyrannosaurus, stegosaurus, triceratops, and apatosaurus. Use the clues to match each child with his or her report.

- Alan's dinosaur starts with a "T".
- Carol's dinosaur is the largest predator below.
- Dean's report was not on a meat-eater.
- Jerry's report was on the largest dinosaur below.

	Tyrannosaurus	Stegosaurus	Triceratops	Apatosaurus
Alan				
Jerry				
Dean				
Carol				

B. Leslie, Kevin, Doug, and Keisha all have different pets. One has a rabbit, one a gerbil, one a dog, and one a cat. Use the clues to match each child with the correct pet.

- The name of the rabbit's owner starts with a "K".
- The dog's owner is not a boy.
- Leslie does not own a cat.
- The smallest pet belongs to Keisha.

	Rabbit	Gerbil	Dog	Cat
Leslie				
Kevin				
Doug				
Keisha				

More I'm Through! What Can I Do? Grade 4 © 2008 Creative Teaching Press

Odd Word Out #1

In each row, all of the words have something in common except one. Find and circle the word that does not belong in each row.

1. calf   kitten   puppy   cub   mule

2. dribble   bunt   homer   strike   inning

3. aunt   father   house   uncle   cousin

4. week   pound   day   month   year

5. pen   pencil   paper   crayon   chalk

6. highway   truck   car   boat   train

Just for Fun—

On the back of your paper, create an Odd Word Out puzzle for a classmate to solve.

Odd Word Out #2

In each row, all of the words have something in common except one. Find and circle the word that does not belong in each row.

1. cloak   lock   flock   clock   knock

2. wharf   whale   which   where   here

3. choose   great   brood   groom   brook

4. chair   shout   change   check   charm

5. chill   spill   squall   drill   skill

6. pop   dad   toot   level   pipe

Just for Fun—

On the back of your paper, create an Odd Word Out puzzle for a classmate to solve.

More I'm Through! What Can I Do? Grade 4 © 2008 Creative Teaching Press

What's for Dessert?

Use the clues to find out what's for dessert. Check off each dessert that doesn't fit the clues until only one is left.

The dessert contains no nuts.

The dessert is not served frozen.

The dessert is not in the shape of a person.

The dessert is not made with chocolate.

The dessert is not wiggly.

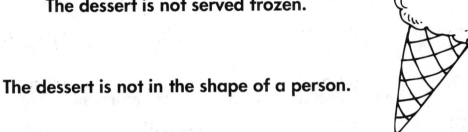

❑ gingerbread cookie   ❑ pecan cookie

❑ cherry gelatin   ❑ chocolate pudding

❑ apple pie   ❑ strawberry ice cream

Name: _____   Date: _____

The Winning Ticket

The student who holds the winning ticket will get a new bike. Use the clues to cross off one ticket at a time until only one is left.

The winning ticket does not have the number 7 in it.
(Cross off the ticket that has the number 7.)

The winning ticket does not end in an odd number.

The winning ticket does not have two of the same numbers next to each other.

The winning ticket does not have more than three numbers.

The number on the winning ticket is _____.

More I'm Through! What Can I Do? Grade 4 © 2008 Creative Teaching Press

Wrigglers

These numbers are wrigglers. Wrigglers all have something in common with each other.

These numbers are not wrigglers.

1. Find and color two more wrigglers below.

2. Draw two other wrigglers in the box.

Name: _____   Date: _____

House Call

Anna, Barb, Carl, Dale, Erin, and Fred all live on the same street. Use the clues below to figure out who lives in which house.

Clues:

- Barb lives between Fred and Dale.
- The sums of the digits in Erin's and Anna's house numbers are the same.
- The digits in Fred's house number are all prime.
- The digits of Dale's and Carl's house numbers are in ascending order.
- Dale lives next door to Barb, but not to Carl.
- The houses next to Anna's do not have chimneys.

Solution:

Anna lives at number _____.   Dale lives at number _____.

Barb lives at number _____.   Erin lives at number _____.

Carl lives at number _____.   Fred lives at number _____.

| 355 | 357 | 361 | 367 | 373 | 379 |

More I'm Through! What Can I Do? Grade 4 © 2008 Creative Teaching Press

Words Add Up #1

In this puzzle, each letter of the alphabet is worth a certain amount of money. Which word below is worth the most? Find out by adding the value of each letter in the words below. Write the sums on the lines. The first one has been done for you.

A = 1 cent	G = 7 cents	M = 13 cents	S = 19 cents	Y = 25 cents
B = 2 cents	H = 8 cents	N = 14 cents	T = 20 cents	Z = 26 cents
C = 3 cents	I = 9 cents	O = 15 cents	U = 21 cents	
D = 4 cents	J = 10 cents	P = 16 cents	V = 22 cents	
E = 5 cents	K = 11 cents	Q = 17 cents	W = 23 cents	
F = 6 cents	L = 12 cents	R = 18 cents	X = 24 cents	

1. m o m _____.13 + .15 + .13_____ total $.41

2. b a b y _____ total _____

3. t o y _____ total _____

4. g i r l _____ total _____

5. b o y _____ total _____

6. a u n t _____ total _____

The word that is worth the most is _____ .

Words Add Up #2

In this puzzle, each letter of the alphabet is worth a certain amount of money. Which word below is worth the most? Find out by adding the value of each letter in the words below. Write the sums on the lines. The first one has been done for you.

A = 1 cent	G = 7 cents	M = 13 cents	S = 19 cents	Y = 25 cents
B = 2 cents	H = 8 cents	N = 14 cents	T = 20 cents	Z = 26 cents
C = 3 cents	I = 9 cents	O = 15 cents	U = 21 cents	
D = 4 cents	J = 10 cents	P = 16 cents	V = 22 cents	
E = 5 cents	K = 11 cents	Q = 17 cents	W = 23 cents	
F = 6 cents	L = 12 cents	R = 18 cents	X = 24 cents	

1. f r o g   .06 + .18 + .15 + .07   total $.46

2. t u r t l e   _____   total _____

3. s n a k e   _____   total _____

4. i n s e c t   _____   total _____

5. s w a m p   _____   total _____

6. w a t e r   _____   total _____

The word that is worth the most is _____ .

Words Add Up #3

In this puzzle, each letter of the alphabet is worth a certain amount of money. Which word below is worth the most? Find out by adding the value of each letter in the words below. Write the sums on the lines. The first one has been done for you.

A = 1 cent	G = 7 cents	M = 13 cents	S = 19 cents	Y = 25 cents
B = 2 cents	H = 8 cents	N = 14 cents	T = 20 cents	Z = 26 cents
C = 3 cents	I = 9 cents	O = 15 cents	U = 21 cents	
D = 4 cents	J = 10 cents	P = 16 cents	V = 22 cents	
E = 5 cents	K = 11 cents	Q = 17 cents	W = 23 cents	
F = 6 cents	L = 12 cents	R = 18 cents	X = 24 cents	

1. c o o l   .03 + .15 + .15 + .12 _____   total $.45

2. g r e a t   _____   total_____

3. n i c e   _____   total_____

4. s u p e r   _____   total_____

5. A - p l u s _____   total_____

6. l o v e l y _____   total_____

The word that is worth the most is _____.

Words Add Up #4

Create your own puzzle by writing six of your favorite words on the lines below. Then use the table to find the value of each letter, and write the numbers below each word. Add up the values for each word to discover which word is worth the most.

A = 1 cent	G = 7 cents	M = 13 cents	S = 19 cents	Y = 25 cents
B = 2 cents	H = 8 cents	N = 14 cents	T = 20 cents	Z = 26 cents
C = 3 cents	I = 9 cents	O = 15 cents	U = 21 cents	
D = 4 cents	J = 10 cents	P = 16 cents	V = 22 cents	
E = 5 cents	K = 11 cents	Q = 17 cents	W = 23 cents	
F = 6 cents	L = 12 cents	R = 18 cents	X = 24 cents	

1. _____   total: _____

   _____

2. _____   total: _____

   _____

3. _____   total: _____

   _____

4. _____   total: _____

   _____

5. _____   total: _____

   _____

6. _____   total: _____

   _____

The word that is worth the most is _____.

More I'm Through! What Can I Do? Grade 4 © 2008 Creative Teaching Press

Parts of a Story Crossword

Unscramble the words below the puzzle. Read the clues. Use the unscrambled words to complete the puzzle.

Across

4. How the story ends

5. The most important moment or turning point of the story

7. The main problem in the story

8. The story line

Down

1. The first part of the story

2. The center part of the story

3. The final part of a story

4. The people in the story

6. Where the story takes place

mlciax _____

nde _____

ltop _____

ddlmie _____

ttsngei _____

cflction _____

ginbenngi _____

rahcacsrte _____

nlouccsoni _____

More I'm Through! What Can I Do? Grade 4 © 2008 Creative Teaching Press

Name: _____ Date: _____

Cinquain Poem
Poetry

Cinquain poetry is a five-line poem that uses a selection of words to describe something.

- Title (one word)
- Two words to describe the title
- Three words that show action about the title
- Four words that show feeling about the title
- A synonym for the title

Circle the poems that are cinquains.

Basketball
Round leather
Bouncing Dribbling Shooting
Play it all day
Roundball

Candy, oh candy
I can't get enough
Candy's so sweet
I just love the stuff

Bedroom
Cozy Colorful
Read Sleep Snack
Like to be there
Mine

Trees are so nice
I never think twice
About resting or sleeping
Beneath one

Choose words and phrases to complete this cinquain. Follow the poetry pattern above.

Cookies

_____ _____

_____ _____ _____

_____ _____ _____ _____

_____

More I'm Through! What Can I Do? Grade 4 © 2008 Creative Teaching Press

Name: _____   Date: _____

Diamante Poem
Descriptive Writing

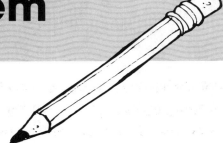

A diamante poem focuses on two opposite or contrasting subjects. The poem consists of 16 words arranged in seven lines to form a diamond shape.

Choose two opposite nouns. Use descriptive words to fill in the diagram to create a diamante poem.

_____
1st noun

_____,   _____
adjective that describes   adjective that describes
1st noun   1st noun

_____,   _____,   _____
verb that tells what   verb that tells what   verb that tells what
1st noun does   1st noun does   1st noun does

_____,   _____,   _____,   _____
noun associated   noun associated   noun associated   noun associated
with 1st noun   with 1st noun   with 2nd noun   with 2nd noun

_____,   _____,   _____
verb that tells what   verb that tells what   verb that tells what
2nd noun does   2nd noun does   2nd noun does

_____,   _____
adjective that describes   adjective that describes
2nd noun   2nd noun

_____
2nd noun

Mall Maze

Alphabetize these words and follow the directions to number the stores as you go through the mall. The first one has been done for you.

1. If *shoe* comes before *slipper* in the dictionary, write the number 9 in the Shoe Salon. If not, write the number 5 in this store.

2. If *emerald* comes before *diamond*, write the number 2 in Jewels by Jenna. If not, write the number 4 in this store.

3. If *hot dog* comes before *hamburger*, write the number 3 in Tutti's Café. If not, write the number 1 in this restaurant.

4. If *basketball* comes before *baseball*, write the number 7 in Sal's Sporting Goods. If not, write the number 8.

5. If *classical* comes after *country*, write the number 15 in the Music Man. If not, write the number 5.

6. If *licorice* comes before *lollipop*, write the number 11 in The Sweet Shop. If not, write the number 6.

7. If *bedding* comes before *bedspread*, write the number 17 in The Home Store. If not, write the number 2.

8. If *fable* comes after *fantasy*, write the number 5 in the Book Barn. If not, write the number 12.

9. If *narcissus* comes before *nasturtium*, write the number 3 in Flora's Flower Cart. If not, write the number 2.

10. If *dalmatian* comes before *dachshund*, write the number 5 in Pets and More. If not, write the number 7.

11. If *card* comes after *candle*, write the number 6 in Card and Gift Shop. If not, write the number 10.

12. If *shirt* comes before *skirt*, write the number 14 in Jay Company Department Store. If not, write the number 6.

13. If *rocking horse* comes before *rocket*, write the number 9 in the Kids' Play Area. If not, write the number 10.

14. If *photographer* comes after *photography*, write the number 7 in the Photo Gallery. If not, write the number 13.

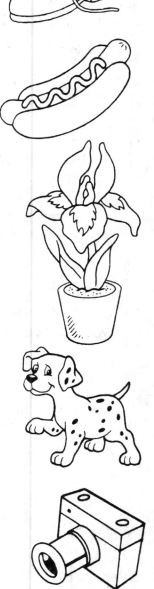

Add the numbers in Music Man, The Home Store, and Book Barn.

Write the sum: _____

Name: _____   Date: _____

Mall Maze

The Home Store

Shoe Salon **9**

Pets and More

Flora's Flower Cart

Photo Gallery

Tutti's Café

Sal's Sporting Goods

Kids' Play Area

The Sweet Shop

Jewels by Jenna

Music Man

Card and Gift Shop

Jay Company Department Store

Book Barn

Name: _____ Date: _____

Geometry Goulash

Follow the directions below using the worksheet on page 67.

1. Write the letter that is not in any of the shapes. _____

2. Write the letter that is only in the oval. _____

3. Write the letter that is only in the oval and the circle. _____

4. Write the letter that is only in the semicircle. _____

5. Write the letter that is only in the oval and the rectangle. _____

6. Write the letter that is only in the square and the rectangle. _____

7. Write the letter that is only in the semicircle and the circle. _____

8. Write the letter that is in the oval, the circle, and the rectangle. _____

9. Write the letter that is in the semicircle, the rectangle, and the circle. _____

10. Write the letters that are only in the triangle. _____

11. Write the letters that are only in the rectangle. _____

12. Write the letter that is only in the circle and the rectangle. _____

13. Write the letters that are in the oval but not in the rectangle. _____

14. Write the letter that is only in the square, the circle, and the rectangle. _____

15. Write the letters that are in the rectangle but not in the square or circle. _____

16. Write the letters that are only in the square. _____

17. Write the letters that are in the rectangle but not in the oval or semicircle. _____

18. Write the letters that are in the circle but not in the square or semicircle. _____

More I'm Through! What Can I Do? Grade 4 © 2008 Creative Teaching Press

Geometry Goulash

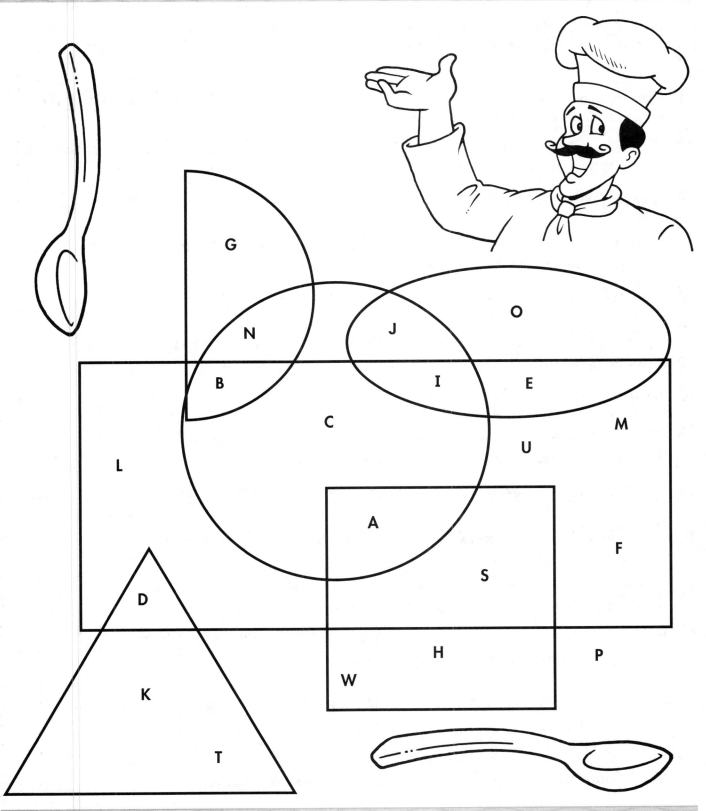

Name: _____ Date: _____

What's for Dinner?

Alphabetize these words and follow the directions to find out what's for dinner. Use the worksheet on page 69. The first one has been done for you.

1. If *pizza* comes before *pie* in the dictionary, write the number 7 in the box under the fish. If not, write the number 12 in the box.

2. If *cheese* comes before *chicken*, write the number 8 in the box under the macaroni and cheese. If not, write the number 2 in the box.

3. If *cherry* comes before *chestnut*, write the number 3 in the box under the hamburger. If not, write the number 4 in the box.

4. If *potato* comes before *porridge*, write the number 2 in the box under the chicken. If not, write the number 5 in the box.

5. If *sandwich* comes after *salmon*, write the number 2 in the box under the salad. If not, write the number 10 in the box.

6. If *peach* comes after *pecan*, write the number 4 in the box under the spaghetti. If not, write the number 7 in the box.

7. If *broccoli* comes before *broth*, write the number 1 in the box under the taco. If not, write the number 5 in the box.

8. If *turkey* comes before *tuna*, write the number 9 in the box under the steak. If not, write the number 6 in the box.

9. If *pickle* comes after *pizza*, write the number 12 in the box under the stew. If not, write the number 11 in the box.

10. If *cheddar* comes before *cheese*, write the number 9 in the box under the pizza. If not, write the number 7 in the box.

11. If *sour cream* comes after *soup*, write the number 4 in the box under the ham. If not, write the number 3 in the box.

12. If *strawberry* comes after *string bean*, write the number 14 in the box under the turkey. If not, write the number 10 in the box.

To find out what's for dinner, add the numbers in the boxes under the steak and the ham. Write this sum on the line: _____

What food has this number and is being served for dinner? _____

More I'm Through! What Can I Do? Grade 4 © 2008 Creative Teaching Press

What's for Dinner?

Draw a Train

1.

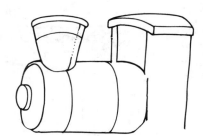

Draw the body of the train as shown.

2.

Add the bell and window. Draw two small wheels and one large back wheel.

3.

Add details to the wheels as shown.

4.

Draw the cowcatcher and details to the side of the train.

Draw your train here. In the background, draw a station full of people waiting for the train.

More I'm Through! What Can I Do? Grade 4 © 2008 Creative Teaching Press

Draw a Robot

1.

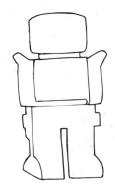

Draw the body of the robot as shown.

2.

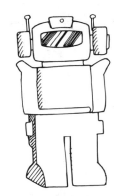

Add the visor and antennae.

3.

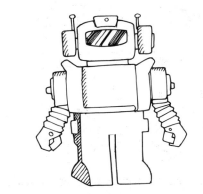

Add the arms and hands.

4.

Draw details to the robot as shown.

Draw your robot here. In the background, draw where your robot is standing.

Think and Color #1

To find out what is in this picture, follow these directions.

1. Color all the spaces with *hexagons* red.
2. Color all the spaces with *octagons* green.
3. Color all the spaces with *trapezoids* orange.
4. Color all the spaces with *pentagons* purple.

5. Color all the spaces with *cylinders* yellow.
6. Color all spaces with *squares* blue.
7. Color all spaces with *isosceles triangles* brown.

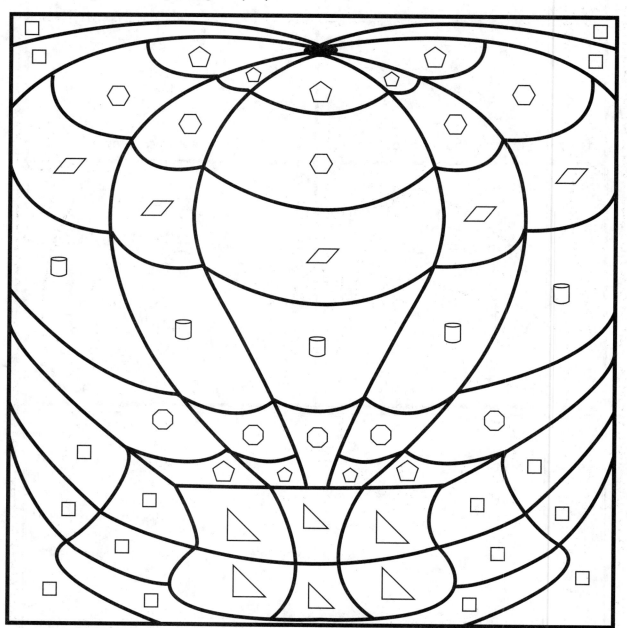

What is it? _____

More I'm Through! What Can I Do? Grade 4 © 2008 Creative Teaching Press

Think and Color #2

To find out what is in this picture, follow these directions.

1. Color all the spaces with *multiples of 5* blue.

2. Color all the spaces with *multiples of 2* green.

3. Color all the spaces with *multiples of 3* dark brown.

4. Color all the spaces with *prime numbers* beige.

5. Color all the spaces with *multiples of 7* yellow.

What is it? _____

Think and Color #3

To find out what is in this picture, follow these directions.

1. Color all the synonyms of *said* red.
2. Color all the synonyms of *pretty* orange.
3. Color all the synonyms of *large* yellow.
4. Color all the synonyms of *cold* brown.

5. Color all the synonyms of *fun* dark green.
6. Color all the synonyms of *angry* blue.
7. Color all the synonyms of *little* light green.

What is it? _____

More I'm Through! What Can I Do? Grade 4 © 2008 Creative Teaching Press

Name: _____   Date: _____

Think and Color #4

To find out what is in this picture, follow these directions.

1. Color all the *continents* orange.
2. Color all the *cities* green.
3. Color all the *countries* gray.

4. Color all the *oceans* brown.
5. Color all the *states* blue.

What is it? _____

Help the Clown!

Help Kiko Find His Mother

Musical Note Maze

Start

Finish!

More I'm Through! What Can I Do? Grade 4 © 2008 Creative Teaching Press

Motorcycle Maze

Complete the Cheerful Crawler

Use the artwork provided below as a guide to help you complete the cheerful crawler.

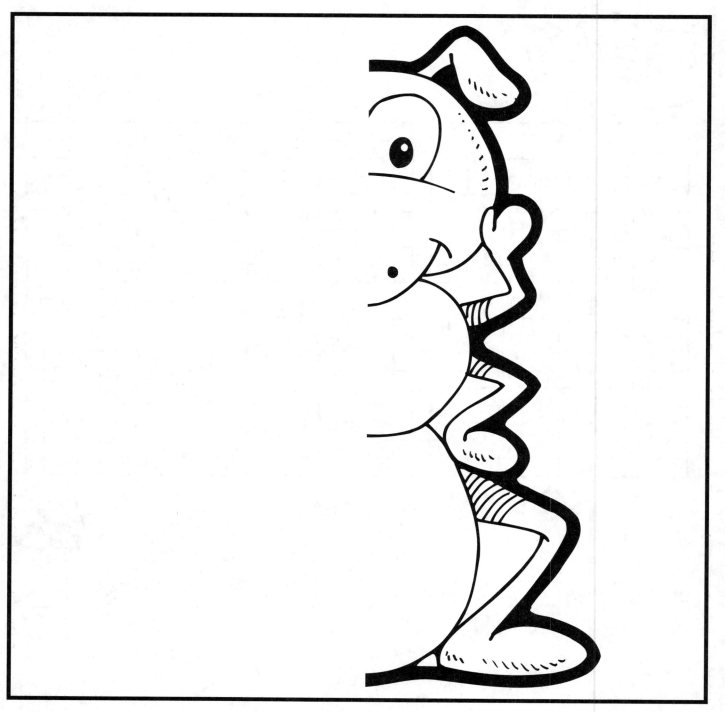

More I'm Through! What Can I Do? Grade 4 © 2008 Creative Teaching Press

Complete the Creepy Crawler

Use the artwork provided below as a guide to help you complete the creepy crawler.

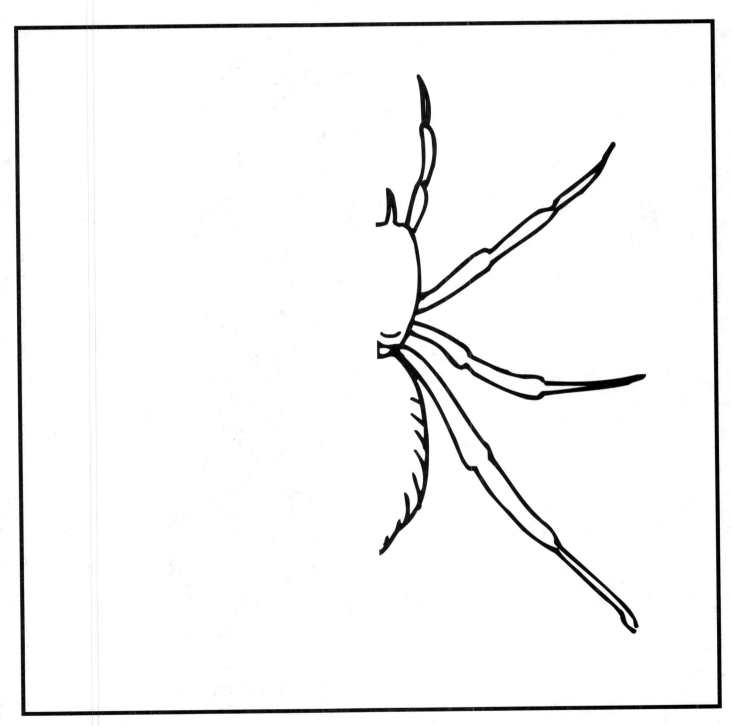

Complete the Rocket Ship

Use the artwork provided below as a guide to help you complete the rocket ship.

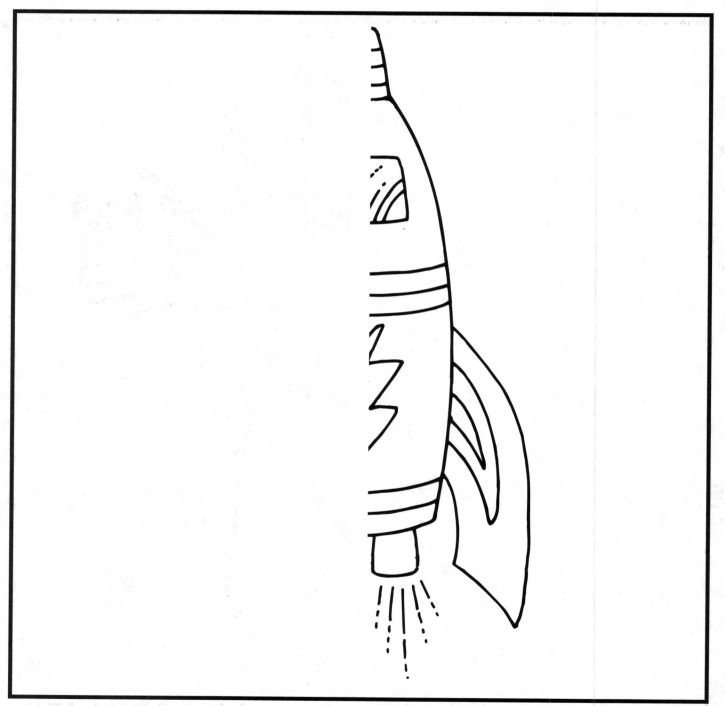

Complete the Scarecrow

Use the artwork provided below as a guide to help you complete the scarecrow.

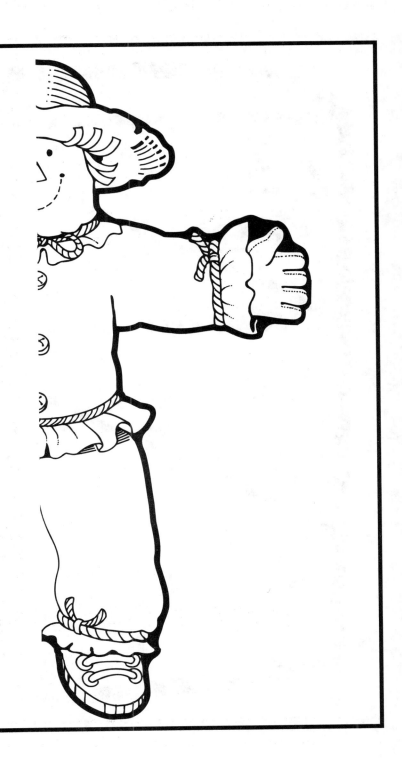

Design a Cereal Box

Design a new type of cereal and give it a "catchy" name. Design the box it comes in and the shape of the cereal. Describe what it tastes like. Then draw some in the bowl beside the box!

More I'm Through! What Can I Do? Grade 4 © 2008 Creative Teaching Press

Design a Sneaker Line

Design your own line of sneakers. Decide on a name for your brand and a logo that will help customers identify your shoes easily. Then draw details on your sneakers and color them in!

Create a Comic Strip #1

Create your own comic strip. Decide on a name for your main character and his or her friends. Think of a problem for your character. Then draw each scene in the comic strip panels. Be creative and have fun!

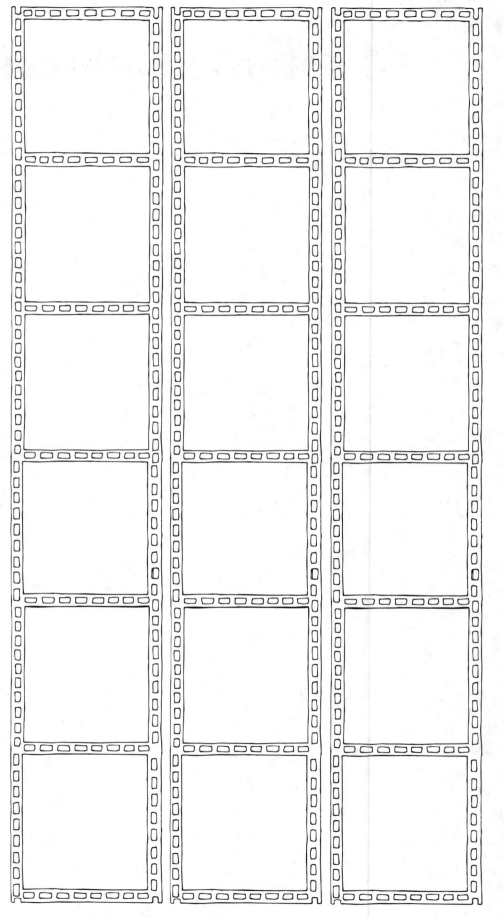

More I'm Through! What Can I Do? Grade 4 © 2008 Creative Teaching Press

Create a Comic Strip #2

Create your own comic strip. Decide on a name for your main character and his or her friends. Think of a problem for your character. Then draw each scene in the comic strip panels. Be creative and have fun!

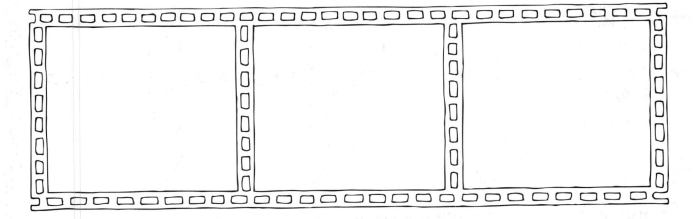

Graph a Picture

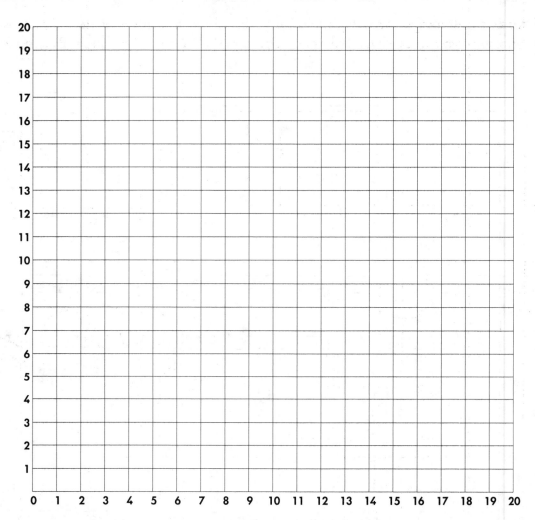

Plot the ordered pairs in the order they are listed below. Connect the dots as you find each one. Start a new figure at each arrow.

➡ (3, 6), (11, 17), (11, 6), (3, 6)

➡ (11, 19),(11, 17), (10, 13), (10, 8), (11, 6), (11, 4)

➡ (11, 4), (3, 4), (5, 2), (7, 3), (10, 2), (11, 3), (12, 2), (15, 3), (16, 2), (17, 4), (12, 4), (11, 4)

➡ (12, 4), (12, 19), (11, 19)

➡ (12, 19), (16, 18), (12, 18), (12, 17), (17, 6)

➡ (12, 6) (13, 8), (13, 13), (12, 17), (12, 6), (17, 6)

Finish the picture with details and color it in!

More I'm Through! What Can I Do? Grade 6 © 2008 Creative Teaching Press

Grid Drawing #1

To make a picture of a flamingo, copy the small drawings into the squares of the grid below. The numbers and letters tell you where to place each drawing. The first one has been done for you.

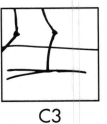

B4

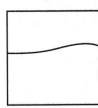

C4

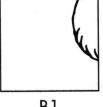

C2

B2

A4

A2

C3

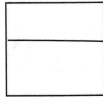

B1

C1

A1

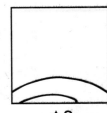

B3

A3

	1	2	3	4
A				
B				
C				

Grid Drawing #2

To make a picture of a butterfly, copy the small drawings into the squares of the grid below. The numbers and letters tell you where to place each drawing. The first one has been done for you.

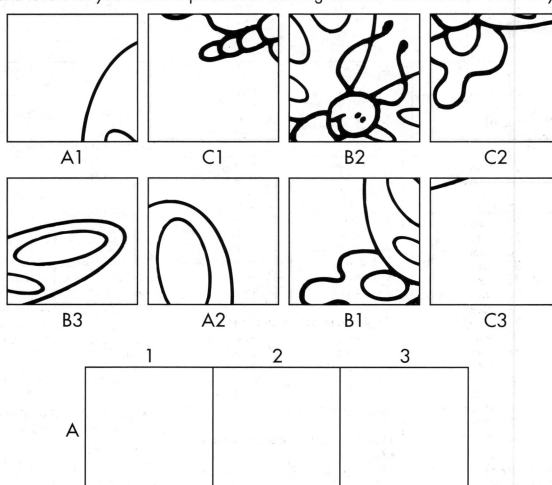

A1 C1 B2 C2

B3 A2 B1 C3

Answer Key

Word Maker #1 (Page 5)
Possible answers include:

1. ant
2. ants
3. antsy
4. ash
5. away
6. bats
7. cyst
8. eats
9. heats
10. hints
11. host
12. hyena
13. jaw
14. nets
15. not
16. pants
17. rats
18. seat
19. soy
20. star
21. stash
22. stew
23. thaw
24. tin
25. watt
26. waits
27. wants
28. what
29. wits
30. yarn

Word Maker #2 (Page 6)
Possible answers include:

1. above
2. acne
3. aloe
4. annoy
5. atom
6. ban
8. bank
9. can
10. cane
11. cave
12. dove
13. enjoy
14. even
15. fan
16. gave
17. have
18. lane
19. love
20. man
21. mane
22. mean
23. mine
24. money
25. monkey
26. move
27. navy
28. omen
29. oven
30. pane
31. ran
32. rank
33. rave
34. rove
35. sank
36. sane
37. save
38. tan
39. tank
40. van
41. venom
42. wave
43. woven

Word Maker #3 (Page 7)
Possible answers include:

1. ale
2. all
3. alm
4. ark
5. aura
6. bud
7. deer
8. dual
9. duel
10. dug
11. eel
12. elk
13. era
14. gals
15. gas
16. glared
17. glee
18. glue
19. greed
20. guide
21. hers
22. lag
23. lake
24. large
25. lug
26. rake
27. red
28. reed
29. residue
30. rug
31. ruled
32. sag
33. sake
34. sale

35. see
36. seek
37. seer
38. shed
39. sled
40. urge

Word Maker #4 (Page 8)
Possible answers include:

1. blob
2. bloom
3. blow
4. blue
5. bone
6. boo
7. boos
8. boom
9. booms
10. bow
11. bowl
12. bowls
13. broom
14. cab
15. calm
16. cob
17. comb
18. cone
19. coo
20. cool
21. coos
22. cow
23. cue
24. eel
25. eels
26. lob
27. loom
28. low
29. lye
30. mob
31. mole
32. money
33. mow
34. obey
35. one
36. orb
37. owe
38. owl
39. slay
40. slob
41. slow
42. smooch
43. sob
44. solo
45. sow
46. web
47. woe
48. womb
49. woo
50. wool

Magic Word Scramble (Page 9)

1. wand
2. spells
3. wizard
4. powerful
5. vanish
6. magician
7. conjure
8. disappear
9. mysterious
10. enchanted

Have a *magical* time!

Natural Disasters Word Scramble (Page 10)

1. tornado
2. landslide
3. eruption
4. volcano
5. tsunami
6. avalanche
7. earthquake
8. typhoon
9. blizzard
10. hurricane

Learn safety *precautions*.

Secret Word #1 (Page 11)
Possible answers include:

3-Letter Words:
alp, ant, apt, bat, cub, lip, oat, pat, sat, tic

4-Letter Words:
acts, also, ants, bail, bias, cuts, icon, last, opal, pact

5-Letter Words:
antic, basil, baton, blast, blunt, cabin, clasp, lions, loans, panic

More than 5 letters:
actions, antics, auction, bionics, biscuit, capitol, caution, cobalt, counts, insult, italics

The secret word is *publications*.

Secret Word #2 (Page 12)
Possible answers include:

3-Letter Words:
one, not, rat, sit, toe, van

4-Letter Words:
acre, cans, coin, icon, iron, love, rare, sail, tail, vane

5-Letter Words:
aisle, alien, alive, earns, evict, laces, ocean, river, scale, stare, vocal, voter

More than 5 letters:
aliens, arrive, carton, coaster, elastic, insert, loaves, nicest, nostril, section, strove, trials

The secret word is *controversial*.

Gingerbread Cookies (Page 13)
Possible answers include:

3-Letter Words:
ace, bar, bin, cab, ode, red, sin, sob

4-Letter Words:
acid, aide, arid, back, bake, bang, king, ring

5-Letter Words:
abide, acorn, aging, bacon, bride, creek, ocean, singe

6-Letter Words:
banker, career, cobras, dragon, engage, ginger, gorged, nicked, robins

More than 6 letters:
aerobic, cookies, earring, ignored, oranges

Banana Cream Pie (Page 14)
Possible answers include:

3-Letter Words:
air, arm, ear, ice, mar, nab, pin, ram

4-Letter Words:
acme, acne, acre, area, bare, beam, cane, earn, main, name, rain

5-Letter Words:
arena, brace, brain, cabin, caper, inner, niece, panic, peace, pecan, price

6-Letter Words:
anemic, banner, camera, canine, empire, maniac, manner, remain

More than 6 letters:
caramel, embrace, penance

Super Scramble (Page 15)
Possible answers include:

hoes (shoe, hose)
eats (teas, seat)
tabs (stab, bats)
parts (strap, tarps, traps)
veil (live, evil, vile)
mean (name, mane, amen)
male (meal, lame)
sever (verse, serve)

Break the Code #1 (Page 16)
They go to the moo-vies.

Break the Code #2 (Page 17)
Nacho Cheese! (Not your cheese)

Break the Code #3 (Page 18)
The North Poll!

Baby Animal Crossword (Page 19)

Across	Down
1. fawn	2. whelp
4. eaglet	3. colt
5. pup	5. poult
6. calf	7. fry
8. cub	10. gosling
9. cygnet	12. chick
11. shoat	
13. kitten	
14. kit	

Step Up #1 (Page 20)
Possible answers include:

1.	2.	3.
dime	**bees**	**cell**
dame	sees	call
date	sews	ball
late	**saws**	**bald**

Step Up #2 (Page 21)
Possible answers include:

1.	2.	3.
sort	**blow**	**tied**
sore	slow	died
pore	flow	dyed
port	flaw	eyed
part	**flat**	**eyes**

Water Sports Word Search (Page 22)
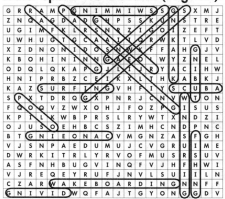

Insect Word Search (Page 23)
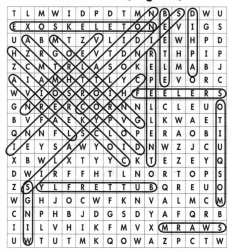

More Than Meets the Eye (Page 24)
There are 80 squares.

Negative and Positive Maze (Page 25)
-1

Negative and Positive Path (Page 26)
22

Computation Maze (Page 27)
144

Amazing Pathways (Page 28)
1. 1 + 11 + 25 + 12 + 36 + 4 + 8 + 3 = 100
2. 100 - 8 - 12 - 27 - 3 - 6 - 26 - 17 = 1
3. 8 + 23 + 18 + 42 + 14 + 27 + 54 + 36 = 222

Find Math Words (Page 29)
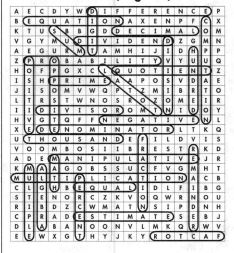

Apple Seed Solutions (Page 30)
John Chapman

Inventor (Page 31)
George Washington Carver

Find a Number (Page 32)
A. 4
B. 14

Find a Rule (Page 33)

1.

■ Input	▲ Output
2	2
8	5
6	4
4	**3**
0	**1**
10	**6**

$$■ + 2 ÷ 2 = ▲$$

2.

■ Input	▲ Output
2	7
3	26
0	-1
4	**63**
5	**124**
6	**215**

$$■^3 −1 = ▲$$
or $■ × ■ × ■ − 1 = ▲$

3.

■ Input	▲ Output
7	3
5	2
3	1
9	**4**
1	**0**
11	**5**

$$■ −1 ÷ 2 = ▲$$

4.

■ Input	▲ Output
12	4
24	7
4	2
16	**5**
20	**6**
0	**1**

$$■ ÷ 4 +1 = ▲$$

5.

■ Input	▲ Output
1	3
2	8
3	15
5	**35**
7	**63**
10	**120**

$$■ + 2 × ■ = ▲$$

Doughnuts (Page 34)
Mrs Kimmel: 24
Mr. Hoff 24
Mrs. Pitt: 12
Mr. Norquist: 5
Mrs. Pfeiffer's tray: 72

It All Adds Up #1 (Page 35)

7	**2**	3
0	4	8
5	6	1

4	6	2
0	5	**7**
8	**1**	3

It All Adds Up #2 (Page 36)

16	**3**	2	13
5	10	11	**8**
9	**6**	**7**	12
4	15	**14**	1

It All Adds Up #3 (Page 37)

2	1	**5**	**6**	4	3
6	**3**	**4**	**5**	**1**	**2**
4	**5**	6	2	**3**	**1**
1	**2**	3	4	**6**	5
5	**6**	**1**	**3**	**2**	**4**
3	4	**2**	**1**	5	6

It All Adds Up #4 (Page 38)

6	**1**	2	4	**5**	**3**
4	**3**	**5**	**6**	**1**	2
5	**2**	6	**1**	3	**4**
3	4	**1**	**2**	6	**5**
1	**5**	**4**	**3**	**2**	6
2	**6**	3	5	**4**	**1**

It All Adds Up #5 (Page 39)

5	**2**	1	6	**4**	3
6	**4**	**3**	**2**	**5**	1
3	1	**4**	**5**	6	**2**
2	**5**	**6**	**1**	3	**4**
4	**6**	**2**	**3**	**1**	5
1	**3**	**5**	4	**2**	**6**

It All Adds Up #6 (Page 40)

9	**2**	**7**	**8**	**5**	**1**	3	**6**	**4**
6	8	1	4	**7**	3	5	9	**2**
5	**4**	**3**	2	**9**	6	**7**	**8**	**1**
7	**9**	5	**6**	3	**2**	4	**1**	8
1	**6**	8	**7**	4	**5**	**2**	**3**	**9**
2	**3**	**4**	**9**	1	**8**	6	5	**7**
8	**1**	**2**	3	**6**	**7**	**9**	**4**	**5**
3	5	9	1	**2**	**4**	8	7	**6**
4	**7**	6	**5**	8	**9**	1	**2**	**3**

It All Adds Up #7 (Page 41)

1	6	9	7	3	2	8	5	4
4	5	3	6	1	8	9	7	2
8	2	7	4	9	5	6	1	3
3	7	8	1	6	9	4	2	5
5	9	1	2	4	7	3	8	6
2	4	6	8	5	3	1	9	7
6	1	5	9	2	4	7	3	8
9	8	2	3	7	6	5	4	1
7	3	4	5	8	1	2	6	9

It All Adds Up #8 (Page 42)

5	7	9	1	6	3	8	2	4
8	4	3	2	9	7	5	6	1
2	1	6	5	8	4	3	9	7
4	6	8	9	2	5	7	1	3
1	2	7	6	3	8	9	4	5
3	9	5	7	4	1	2	8	6
6	3	4	8	7	2	1	5	9
9	8	1	3	5	6	4	7	2
7	5	2	4	1	9	6	3	8

Ice Cream Scoops (Page 43)

1. 1,468
2. 8,641
3. 9
4. 7
5. 2
6. 18
7. 48
8. 192
9. 1,468

Taxi Numbers (Page 44)

1. 2,357
2. 7,532
3. 8
4. 5
5. 4
6. 15
7. 6
8. 10.5
9. 3,572

See-Saw Solutions (Page 45)
Possible answers may include:

1. Balance: *jet*
   Category: *things you can fly*
2. Balance: *meters*
   Category: *units of measure*
3. Balance: *feet*
   Category: *things that come in pairs*
4. Balance: *comets*
   Category: *things found in space*
5. Balance: *pudding*
   Category: *desserts*
6. Balance: *ball*
   Category: *things related to baseball*

What's Missing? (Page 46)
Possible answers may include:

1. Eve (3-letter name beginning with "e")
2. arrow (5-letter word beginning with "a")
3. eagle (5-letter word beginning with "e")
4. meant (word that begins with "m" and ends with "nt")
5. parrot (2-syllable word beginning with "p")
6. Oscar (name that begins with "O". Each name skips one more letter than previous. Skip 1 letter, skip 2 letters, etc...)

Elimination (Page 47)
Cross out:

1. throw (not a sport)
2. building (not a room)
3. wet (not a drink)
4. Perot (not a president)
5. Aldrich (not an early explorer)
6. menu (not something you renew)
7. bicycle (not something you inflate)
8. fur (not something hard)
9. smile (not a feeling or emotion)

Favorite Sports (Page 48)
Pauli—tennis
Bob—soccer
Deanne—basketball
Paul—volleyball

Which Bicycle? (Page 49)
Melanie—white
Leanne—yellow
Mark—green
Susan—red

Solving Puzzles (Page 50)
A. Alan—triceratops
   Jerry—apatosaurus
   Dean—stegosaurus
   Carol—tyrannosaurus

B. Leslie—dog
   Kevin—rabbit
   Doug—cat
   Keisha—gerbil

Odd Word Out #1 (Page 51)

1. mule (not a baby animal name)
2. dribble (not a baseball word)
3. house (not the name of a relative)
4. pound (not part of a calendar; not a measurement of time)
5. paper (not something to write or draw with)
6. highway (not a type of transportation)

Odd Word Out #2 (Page 52)

1. cloak (doesn't end with -ock; doesn't rhyme with the other words)
2. here (doesn't begin with wh-)
3. great (doesn't have double o's)
4. shout (doesn't begin with ch-)
5. squall (doesn't end with -ill; doesn't rhyme with the other words)
6. pipe (isn't spelled the same forwards and backwards or doesn't begin and end with the same letter)

What's for Dessert? (Page 53)
The dessert is apple pie.

The Winning Ticket (Page 54)
The number on the winning ticket is 684.

Wrigglers (Page 55)

1. 15 and 18 (multiples of three)
2. Possible answers include 24 and 27, 30 and 33.

House Call (Page 56)
Anna lives at number 373.
Barb lives at number 361.
Carl lives at number 379.
Dale lives at number 367.
Erin lives at number 355.
Fred lives at number 357.

Words Add Up #1 (Page 57)

1. $.41
2. $.30
3. $.60
4. $.46
5. $.42
6. $.56

The word that is worth the most is *toy*.

Words Add Up #2 (Page 58)

1. $.46
2. $.96
3. $.50
4. $.70
5. $.72
6. $.67

The word that is worth the most is *turtle*.

Words Add Up #3 (Page 59)

1. $.45
2. $.51
3. $.31
4. $.79
5. $.69
6. $.64

The word that is worth the most is *lovely*.

Words Add Up #4 (Page 60)

Answers will vary.

Parts of a Story Crossword (Page 61)

Across

4. conclusion
5. climax
7. conflict
8. plot

Down

1. beginning
2. middle
3. end
4. characters
6. setting

Cinquain Poem (Page 62)

Basketball and *Bedroom* should be circled. Student cinquains will vary.

Diamante Poem (Page 63)

Answers will vary.

Mall Maze (Pages 64–65)

1. 9
2. 4
3. 1
4. 8
5. 5
6. 11
7. 17
8. 12
9. 3
10. 7
11. 6
12. 14
13. 10
14. 13

The answer is 34.

Geometry Goulash (Pages 66–67)

1. P
2. O
3. J
4. G
5. E
6. S
7. N
8. I
9. B
10. K, T
11. L, U, M, F
12. C
13. J, O
14. A
15. L, U, M, F, E, D
16. W, H
17. L, C, A, S, U, M, F, D
18. C, I, J

What's for Dinner (Pages 68–69)

chicken–5
pizza–9
hamburger–3
salad–2
fish–12
spaghetti–7
macaroni and cheese–8
taco–1
stew–11
ham–4
turkey–10
steak–6

10; Turkey

Draw a Train (Page 70)

Drawing may vary but should reflect following directions.

Draw a Robot (Page 71)

Drawing may vary but should reflect following directions.

Think and Color #1 (Page 72)

(hot air balloon)

Think and Color #2 (Page 73)

(monkey)

Think and Color #3 (Page 74)

(flower)

Think and Color #4 (Page 75)

(globe)

Help the Clown! (Page 76)

Help Kiko Find His Mother (Page 77)

Complete the Cheerful Crawler (Page 80)
Drawing should be symmetrical.

Complete the Creepy Crawler (Page 81)
Drawing should be symmetrical.

Complete the Rocket Ship (Page 82)
Drawing should be symmetrical.

Complete the Scarecrow (Page 83)
Drawing should be symmetrical.

Design a Cereal Box (Page 84)
Design will vary.

Design a Sneaker Line (Page 85)
Designs will vary.

Create a Comic Strip (Page 86–87)
Comic strips will vary.

Graph a Picture (Page 88)

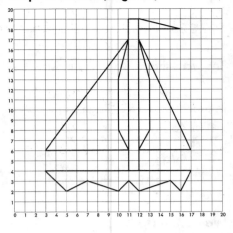

Grid Drawing #1 (Page 89)

Grid Drawing #2 (Page 90)

Musical Note Maze (Page 78)

Motorcycle Maze (Page 79)